KU-070-659

GILES

The Collection 2021

compiled by John Field

EXPRESS NEWSPAPERS

hamlyn

An Hachette UK Company
www.hachette.co.uk

First published in Great Britain in 2020 by Hamlyn,
a division of Octopus Publishing Group Ltd, Carmelite House,
50 Victoria Embankment, London EC4Y 0DZ
www.octopusbooks.co.uk

Cartoons
British Cartoon Archive

Cartoons supplied by British Cartoon Archive
Cartoons compiled by John Field

ISBN 978 0 60063 478 2

A CIP catalogue record for this book is available from the British Library.

Printed and bound in China

10 9 8 7 6 5 4 3 2 1

Contents

Lord Beaverbrook,
see page 16

Introduction: Famous Faces

This year's *Giles: The Collection* features Giles's work on famous people, including various well-known politicians and celebrities, infamous people of the time and members of the Royal Family. Giles featured a huge variety of well-known people over the years and, in turn, many famous faces have sung his praises as the greatest cartoonist of his time. Here are just a selection of Giles' accolades:

Lord Beaverbrook, publisher of the *Daily Express* and the *Sunday Express*, in 1953
"Giles has an immense following. His cartoons give joy to millions of *Express* readers. They are extensively reproduced in the United States and syndicated in the British Empire. They brighten the pages of newspapers at home and abroad. The demand for them is insatiable. What is the secret? It is this: Giles has a sardonic humour which appeals because he always keeps close to life of the street and the farm. He depicts the attitudes of ordinary people."

Pietro Annigoni, artist, in 1956
"He is wonderful, your Giles. I saw him first four years ago when I arrived in England. I always look for his cartoons. We now have them reprinted in Italian papers. He is very popular there [...] It is a pity that we do not also have cartoonists like Giles. Because he is such a fine artist, such a fine draughtsman, as well as a very funny cartoonist. I appreciate his talent as well as his humour."

Dame Margot Fonteyn, ballerina, in 1959
"Very few men can see clearly all the imperfections of face and form in the world yet still retain an indulgent affection for humanity. Such a person is Giles. He must be a very compassionate man. Anyone else with his needle-sharp eyes would find it hard not to be biting in their humour but he mocks us only very gently."

Sir Spike Milligan, comedian, in 1962
"I'm not going to be funny about Giles – because that would invoke disaster. I can't compete with the devastating humour he produces, which embrace all stratas of life, and makes them hilarious. What endears me most to him is his gentleness, yet he packs a bigger punch with a feather than our customary satirists do with a sledge hammer."

Sir Sean Connery, actor, in 1966
"The *Giles Annual* is always a marvellous yearly backlog of what we have all been though and how absurd, mad, sad, ridiculous and funny, life, politics, religion and the world is. This year it is my turn to thank him.

Michael Bentine CBE, comedian and actor, in 1970
"When I was a very young and inexperienced combatant in the last war, Giles had a special meaning for me. Somehow, magically, he took

the terror out of it all. His Hitler and Mussolini were wonderfully funny caricatures which cut the monsters down to size. Today, over twenty-five years later, Giles is still tilting at windmills, cutting the pompous, the vain-glorious and self-important down to their right proportions."

Sir Michael Parkinson, broadcaster, journalist and author, in 1973
"To say that Giles is a good cartoonist is like saying that George Gershwin wrote some nice tunes or Garfield Sobers is a lovely cricketer. It misses the fundamental point of the man – that he is a genius [...] A catalogue of Giles cartoons is a history of our time, revealing not simply the mood of the moment but also charting our changing environment [...] His humour is never hurtful or vicious. It touches all of us who are possessed of that most important human quality, the ability to laugh at ourselves."

Eric Morecambe OBE, comedian, in 1976
"Let me tell you, and I mean this in all seriousness, folks, that Giles is one of the great humourists of all time. I admire and envy his talent. It's a wonderful gift to be able to make people laugh and to manage it every day by the use of a pencil and a dozen or so carefully chosen words is doubly clever [...] Every one of his cartoons is like a five-minute television sketch. There is so much to find in the background after you have had your initial laugh at the main joke line."

Frank Sinatra, actor, in 1979
"To Giles – who has been so kind to me through the years and who I believe to be one of the funniest men in the world – affectionately, Francis Albert."

Sir John Betjeman, poet, writer and broadcaster, in 1983
"The subtle humour of Giles cartoons is a gentle reflection of the absurdities of our age. I am honoured to have been the subject of a cartoon from the past, loved by Giles, depicting a workman climbing from his demolition machine saying to his foreman 'I've just knocked down John Betjeman'. It makes me very glad that I should be singled out as a public monument due for demolition, that puts me in the top class, architecturally."

Dame Joan Collins, actress, author and columnist, in 1987
"Giles. Whenever I hear that name, it conjures up visions of England. An England that hasn't changed very much since I was a child giggling at the antics of Grandma, Mum and Dad, the kids and all the other favourite beloved characters that he created so brilliantly. A Giles cartoon isn't like any other cartoon. It is deeply

Prince Charles, see page 83

detailed with subtly hidden humours lurking in every corner. It is indeed a veritable gem to study and laugh at with the morning tea."

Magnus Magnusson KBE, journalist, writer and television presenter, in 1990

"It's the Giles family that gets me. They are so *family.* They are so gloriously, anarchically *his* that there could be no other family like them anywhere, and yet they somehow manage to be everybody's family. Nobody's granny could be as awful as Grandma Giles, and yet there is something about her that is every indomitable granny who ever lived. The long-suffering mother, the self-absorbed teenagers, the hypochondriac Auntie Vera, the demonic children and their hapless pets – they are all hilariously over the top, yet with all the elements of family life so sharply sensed and so utterly recognisable that the heart warms while the stomach heaves with laughter."

HRH Prince Charles, in 1996

"It is an enormous sadness that, with the death of Giles in 1995, this will be the last traditional *Giles Annual* to be published. For countless people who, like myself, have grown up in Britain since the Second World War, 'Giles' has been a much loved 'institution'. I myself always looked forward to his cartoons. Somehow they captured, almost unerringly, the mood of the nation. His gently wicked but never vindictive humour, wherever it was applied – to politics, my family, the day-to-day incidents and dramas of life in Britain and abroad – endeared him to all of us in a way that no other cartoonist has achieved this century."

A note on Giles himself

Through his illustrious career at the *Express*, Giles soon became a household name and would occasionally insert himself into a cartoon, either as the focal point or more discreetly lurking on the sidelines, as a game for readers to spot the artist. A number of these cartoons have been featured and show that even the artist himself is not immune from his own gentle mockery.

The substantial admiration for Giles's work, shown above by the great and the good, remains as strong today as it ever was and he is universally admired for the manner in which he was able to capture the humour and idiosyncrasies of our country's life covering five decades. In fact, the great wealth of his cartoons has allowed the prolific artist to continue to delight today, as *Giles* has become an annual publication event looked forward to by so many people, famous or not.

John Field

Politicians

In fact, Churchill wished to go to sea on HMS *Belfast* and observe the progress of the D-Day landings, but the King stopped him by threatening to also go.

"Didn't the B.B.C. say that he went back on Tuesday?"

Daily Express, 15 June 1944

Berchtesgaden, in the Bavarian Alps, Germany, was one of Hitler's homes and main headquarters during World War II. At the time, the three great Allied war leaders, Churchill, Roosevelt and Stalin – shown inside the taxi – were gathered at the Yalta Conference (4–11 February 1945) in the Crimea to discuss the post-war reorganization of Germany and Europe.

"Hey you – how far is this Berchtesgaden?"

Daily Express, 6 February 1945

12 Sir Stafford Cripps, President of the Board of Trade, was part of a British government delegation visiting India to discuss Indian independence. Perhaps Gandhi, remembering the British climate from his visit to Lancashire in the autumn of 1931, felt that if he was required to visit the UK again as part of the negotiations, he would be better prepared this time.

"Before we get down to business, Stafford, I suppose you couldn't let me have a couple of clothing coupons?"

Daily Express, 21 February 1946

This was at the Labour Party Annual Conference in Scarborough where, obviously, Prime Minister Clement Attlee was feeling a little uneasy about his future. Waiting impatiently outside for him are, from left to right, Herbert Morrison, Deputy Prime Minister, Aneurin Bevan, Minister of Health, and Ernest Bevin, Foreign Secretary.

"Come on, Clem, we can't wait all day!"

Daily Express, 21 May 1948

14 Ernest Bevin, Clement Attlee and Herbert Morrison, outside the Houses of Parliament – maybe it was a case of mistaken identity by the Downing Street police squad or maybe the squad was displeased with the way the country was being governed.

"That's what comes of arming the Downing Street Police – little holes in our hats."

Sunday Express, 15 May 1949

Settling down for the night in Central Park in New York, Sir Stafford Cripps (Chancellor of the Exchequer) and Ernest Bevin (Secretary of State for Foreign Affairs) were seeking support from the United States of America during a period of extreme financial problems at home.

"Staff – considering that we have just saved the country from financial ruin, do you think Clem would mind if we stayed in an hotel tonight?"

Daily Express, 15 September 1949

16 A high-level political meeting hosted by the Giles family. From left – Lord Beaverbrook (making friends with Grandma), eldest son George (greeting comrade Hewlett Johnson, the "Red Dean of Canterbury"), Anthony Eden (Deputy Leader of the Opposition), father, Clement Attlee (Prime Minister), Aneurin Bevan (Minister of Health) – with sickly Vera taking advantage of his presence, Winston Churchill (Leader of the Opposition), Ernest Bevin (Foreign Secretary) and Sir Stafford Cripps (Chancellor of the Exchequer), interspersed with various members of the Giles family. The thrower of the turnip is unknown.

"Put the kettle on, Mother – Dad's brought home some gentlemen to discuss the election date."

Daily Express, 11 October 1949

Aneurin Bevan, at the Tower of London, preparing for a difficult meeting with the press. As the Minister for Health, Bevan was probably expecting some difficult questions about the recent decision giving the National Health Service powers to levy charges for prescriptions.

"I'm shortly attending a meeting of Fleet Street Journalists – these are my measurements…"

Daily Express, 13 December 1949

18 The Groundnut Scheme was started in 1947 to grow peanuts in the state of Tanganyika (present-day Tanzania) as a contribution to both African and British economies. John Strachey, Minister of Food at the time, supported the scheme and in April 1946, the British Government authorized a mission to identify suitable sites. The new Minister of Food, Maurice Webb, took over but the scheme was unsuccessful and was eventually abandoned four years later.

"Over to you, Maurice......"

Daily Express, 2 March 1950

A mix-up outside the Houses of Parliament – among the cattle, from left, Ernest Bevin, Aneurin Bevan, Herbert Morrison, Anthony Eden and Churchill (possibly wearing a reference to his part-American heritage).

"Same old mix-up as last year – opening Parliament the same week as the Dairy Show."

Daily Express, 26 October 1950

20 Dr Charles Hill (in the chair) was the British Medical Association Secretary who negotiated with Aneurin Bevan, Minister of Health, to ensure GPs did not simply become salaried employees – this probably caused difficulties between them (note the picture on the wall). Four days earlier, Bevan became the Minister of Labour and, perhaps, Giles is suggesting that he is seeking revenge. It is unclear why Churchill enters the cartoon in a nurse's uniform.

"Cheek! Note from the new Minister of Labour directing me for work in the mines."

Sunday Express, 21 January 1951

This shows Ernest Bevin being held back by a group of Labour MPs, including Clement Attlee (Prime Minister), Aneurin Bevan, John Strachey and Herbert Morrison (with the glasses), five days before Morrison replaced Bevin as Secretary of State for Foreign Affairs – a tricky situation for all involved.

Sunday Express, 4 March 1951

Prime Minister Clement Attlee and Herbert Morrison – who was responsible for the Festival of Britain, which was being held at that time in Battersea, London – talk to King Farouk of Egypt. There was increasing tension between the two countries, which led to the Suez Crisis.

Lord Festival gets tough... / ...tersea Park lake.

Daily Express, 17 July 1951

Aneurin Bevan, Minister of Labour, visits Yugoslavia's Communist President, Josip Tito. Bevan's boss, Prime Minister Clement Attlee, and Tito's fellow political thinker, the Soviet leader Joseph Stalin, are equally suspicious of what they are up to.

Sunday Express, 29 July 1951

Churchill was in Washington to discuss Anglo-American relations. Eleven days later, in a speech to the US Senate, he said: "Bismark once said that the supreme fact of the 19th century was that Britain and America spoke the same language. Let us make sure that the supreme fact of the 20th century is that we tread the same path." Joseph Stalin was the Premier and Andrey Vishinsky the Foreign Minister of the Soviet Union at that time.

"How d'you like that – Joe and Vishinsky called at No.10 for a peace conference – didn't know I was out."

Daily Express, 6 January 1952

Jack Hylton was an English pianist, composer, band leader and impresario. At the time, he wrote an article in the *Daily Mirror* entitled "Why I want to be an MP". Churchill is concerned that if Hylton were to be successful, he would wish to apply his "showman's" promotional talents to Parliament.

"TODAY'S THOUGHT for those who are already legislators."

Daily Express, 18 February 1954

The Cold War between the East and the West was at its height. While addressing Western ambassadors at a reception in Moscow three years earlier, the Soviet First Secretary, Nikita Khrushchev, had stated, “We will bury you!”. Here, Khrushchev does not seem too pleased. He was in Los Angeles, on an 11-day tour of the United States, where he was reported to be “outraged” by a speech made by the LA Mayor.

“Gentlemen, I think the World will agree that in welcoming Mr. Krushchev we have ended the Cold War by making it boiling hot.”

Daily Express, 22 September 1959

Khrushchev just dropping down onto the Capitol Hill car park would have surprised a lot more people than just the police officer. This was in the middle of the space race between the US and the Soviet Union. Four days earlier, Russia had surprised the US with a major leap forward in the race – a space flight by Russian cosmonaut Gherman Titov in spacecraft *Vostok 2*. Titov was in space for a full day and made 17 orbits of the Earth.

"Our Chief of Aeronautical Engineering says the Russian controlled Space Landing is a lot of 'malarkey' and he should know."

Daily Express, 10 August 1961

28 This cartoon appeared on Guy Fawkes Day, reminding us of the earlier attempt to blow up Parliament. Sir Alec Douglas-Home (in the cap) had been Prime Minister for only 16 days. Having resigned his peerage to become PM, his appointment was controversial and his manner was considered by some to be aloof and old-fashioned.

"I hope ye're no' offended, Sir Alec – my wee bairns are a wee bit radically minded."

Daily Express, 5 November 1963

Barbara Castle was one of the most prominent female politicians in the history of the Labour Party. In 1966, despite her being a non-driver, Prime Minister Harold Wilson made her Minister for Transport and, shortly afterwards, she called for "a profound change in public attitudes" to curtail increasing road fatalities. A week before this cartoon appeared, she had brought in the roadside breathalyser test and, later, seat belts – neither of which were popular with all drivers.

"Getting Mrs. Castle honked and selling her one of our Super Z Type Sports may not be funny or clever, but it's damn good salesmanship."

Daily Express, 17 October 1967

Denis Healey (centre), Secretary of State for Defence, was visiting Cambridge during a period of student unrest. His car was pelted with eggs and attempts were made to overturn it. Five people were arrested.

"To take action against the students who mobbed Mr. Healey would not be desirable or practicable."
(The Revd Donald Cupitt, Senior Proctor at Cambridge.)

Daily Express, 12 March 1968

When aggrieved about something, Grandma obviously believes in "going to the top". Here, she has captured Barbara Castle – who was just three weeks into her new job as First Secretary of State – in order to pursue her complaint.

"It's the old fool who said she'd report us to Barbara Castle for putting a penny on her embrocation."

Daily Express, 30 April 1968

Rab Butler (in the gown) was a leading Conservative MP, eventually becoming Father of the House. After his retirement from politics, he became Master of Trinity College, Cambridge in 1965. Prince Charles became a student at Trinity and his formal investiture as Prince of Wales took place six months after this cartoon appeared.

"Ask his Royal Highness to come to my office when he's finished his solo flight."

Daily Express, 16 January 1969

Lord Hailsham, Shadow Home Secretary under Edward Heath's Conservative Party, in Opposition at this time – possibly all politicians look the same to an angry bull.

"It's about time you taught that wee bull of yours the difference between the Government and the Opposition."

Daily Express, 3 February 1970

Prime Minister Harold Wilson (on the left) and Edward Heath (on the right) vent their anger at the way politicians are portrayed by political cartoonists – presumably including Giles himself – in front of the National Portrait Gallery, which was hosting a cartoon exhibition. Five weeks after this cartoon, the Conservatives won the General Election and Heath took over from Wilson as Prime Minister.

"You are charged with unlawfully entering the National Portrait Gallery carrying offensive weapons with intent to commit grievous bodily harm...."

Daily Express, 12 May 1970

Giles shows a motley group of British hierarchy, including Prime Minister Edward Heath, being hijacked, following an earlier similar fate relating to a small group of sailors in Ireland.

"If you're thinking hijacking three English sailors was a masterpiece of strategy then, O'Flannagan..."

Daily Express, 9 July 1970

Anthony Barber, the Chancellor of the Exchequer, under Edward Heath, on Budget Day, 1971 – a difficult period with a slowing economy and increasing industrial unrest. Obviously, Grandma was not happy with things.

"Hold tight, sir."

Daily Express, 30 March 1971

This cartoon shows Prime Minister Edward Heath out on his 42-foot yacht *Morning Cloud*. A few weeks later, he steered the British Admiral's Cup team to victory at its helm – the first British Prime Minister to win a major trophy while in office. No evidence has been found that Heath was ever expecting a visit from China's Chairman Mao.

"Ted, you remember you invited Mao over to Number 10 for peace talks?"

Sunday Express, 18 July 1971

Harold Wilson, nursing his leg, was the Leader of the Opposition at this time, having lost his role as Prime Minister to Edward Heath, obviously a right-footer, the previous summer.

"That's for twisting my wrist when you presented me with that honorary degree last Saturday."

Daily Express, 2 November 1971

Outside the Houses of Parliament. An infestation of mice resulted in MPs demanding action. This is Giles's suggestion for an answer to the problem, involving the Prime Minister, Edward Heath.

"Great for the old image – 'P.M. saves nation cost of cat'."

Daily Express, 14 March 1972

Edward Heath enjoys a popular song of the time.

"Do you think I would leave you walking... When there's room on my horse for two..."

Sunday Express, 3 December 1972

Sir Gerald Nabarro (Nab), a Conservative politician, with a drink in his hand, was strongly opposed to one of the passions of pipe-smoking Harold Wilson, Opposition Leader, in the next room. No doubt, however, he accepted the cigar-smoking habit of one of his own party's most-loved grandees, pictured above his head.

"Nab, before you let off any more hot air about Opposition Leader's obnoxious habit of smoking..."

Daily Express, 13 February 1973

 At the time, Prime Minister Edward Heath had received, as a present from China, two giant pandas – Ching Ching and Chia Chia. He passed them on to London Zoo. At the same time, the Leader of the Liberal Party, Jeremy Thorpe, was going through a rather tumultuous period in his private life and, maybe, he was concerned about the future wellbeing of a pet hamster if ever he was not free to look after it himself.

"A Mr. Thorpe wants to know if we've got a show-cage for his hamster."

Daily Express, 17 September 1974

In Parliament, Barbara Castle MP, as Secretary of State for Social Services, was in the middle of a difficult period of negotiations regarding the medical profession's pay and contracts in the National Health Service. The dentist seems pleased to be able to deal with her.

"A Mrs. B. C-A-S-T-L-E. Toothache."

Daily Express, 4 January 1975

44 This was during the run-up to the Conservative Party leadership elections the following month, which both Margaret Thatcher and Edward Heath were contesting. It coincided with a period of severe fuel shortages, when people were encouraged to use car-sharing schemes.

"Margaret, I have performed my social obligations and picked you up, but let there be no misapprehensions about you being my mate."

Daily Express, 28 January 1975

Margaret Thatcher, placing a bet in the Conservative Party leadership contest at Eastbourne, with the main contender at the time, Edward Heath, obviously not sure what to do. Heath withdrew after the first ballot and Thatcher beat Willie Whitelaw in the second ballot.

Daily Express, 4 February 1975

46 Margaret Thatcher is warmly greeted by Willie Whitelaw at the Conservative Party Conference in Eastbourne. Both were seeking to replace Edward Heath as Leader. This was a period of high inflation in Britain.

"What he's really saying is 'Maggie, I know a little shop that will let you have as many crates of tinned food as you can store at 10 per cent off.'"

Daily Express, 11 February 1975

This was less than two weeks after the Conservative Party Leadership election, which Margaret Thatcher won. The party grandees are debating her apparent reluctance to appear on television and ways of raising her public profile by using radio programme personalities, or their relatives, popular at that time. Giles shows her as Britannia, looking down upon the discussion."

"What do you mean she couldn't do worse than going on the Jimmy Young Prog? She could appear on TV making gravy with Mrs. Tony Blackburn."

Daily Express, 21 February 1975

48 This related to a national referendum to gauge support for the country's continued membership of the European Community, as the EU was then known. Harold Wilson, the Prime Minister, recommended that the Government should support Britain's continued membership, and the public referendum, on 5 June, voted, by a margin of two-to-one, to stay.

"Dear Margaret, I hope you won't take it amiss if I just say, 'Let the better man win today.'"

Daily Express, 22 May 1975

Five months earlier, Margret Thatcher had succeeded Edward Heath as Leader of the Opposition. It has been said that Heath was never reconciled to Thatcher's leadership but maybe, here, he is wishing to make friends with her. It follows the European referendum, which took place one month earlier and in which both supported staying in the Union.

"I'm afraid she left by the other door, Sir."

Daily Express, 7 July 1975

Although Edward Heath had expected to win the Conservative Party leadership in an election the previous February, he lost to Thatcher. He was probably still feeing sore at this meeting.

"He only promised he wouldn't speak while Margaret Thatcher was speaking."

Daily Express, 7 October 1975

Britain was going through a very difficult period, with high inflation, industrial disputes and widespread strikes leading to the 1978 Winter of Discontent. Prime Minister James Callaghan was visiting Washington to discuss the financial situation with US President Jimmy Carter and was probably in no mood to hand out money.

"My brother-in-law in the British Police cabled me: 'Don't expect no gratuities'."

Daily Express, 9 March 1977

The Budget turned out better than Butch, the family dog, anticipated. Denis Healey, the Chancellor of the Exchequer, stated that, for once, he was not asking anyone to make any sacrifices and, instead, offered £2,400 million in tax cuts to stimulate the economy. Liberal MPs were delighted, claiming to have influenced the Chancellor during their political alliance with Labour, but Conservative leader Margaret Thatcher considered that the tax cuts would soon disappear without being noticed.

"Shut up, Butch, wait till we see what he does tomorrow."

Daily Express, 10 April 1978

At the TUC conference in Brighton, Prime Minister James Callaghan, sang a song about "the bride being left at the altar". The cartoon shows Leader of the Opposition Margaret Thatcher outdoing her rival's attempt at entertainment and, in fact, she comfortably won the General Election the following May. The bus passengers include a number of Labour politicians, with Michael Foot, Leader of the House of Commons, on the front left.

"Anything we can do she can do better – it had to come."

Daily Express, 7 September 1978

No doubt Grandma's homemade wine is a severe test of anyone's admiration of our country.

"We'll see if Uncle Walt still admires us British after a sample of Grandma's homemade wine."

Daily Express, 14 September 1978

This cartoon appeared at the time of the meeting discussing Rhodesian independence in Lancaster House, London. On the following 21 December, an agreement was signed which declared a ceasefire, ending the war in Rhodesia. This led to the end of British rule and the creation and recognition of the Republic of Zimbabwe. At the front of the group is Joshua Nkomo, of the Zimbabwe African People's Union, and further back is Robert Mugabe, then leader of the Patriotic Front.

"Can he have a couple of dozen as souvenirs for a few of his friends back home?"

Daily Express, 11 September 1979

This shows MPs returning to Parliament after the Summer Recess. Michael Foot (with the stick) was about to take over leadership of the Labour Party from James Callaghan. Following a comment by a Conservative MP, Foot gradually acquired the nickname "Worzel Gummidge" in the press, reflecting his rural appearance. This probably explains the mole – but I wonder, also, if a number of "leaks" of information were happening at that time?

"Excuse me, Sir."

Daily Express, 28 October 1980

Willie Whitelaw, Home Secretary, whose responsibilities include internal affairs in England and Wales, having to be "stamped" before he can enter the Royal Enclosure at Royal Ascot. This was a during period of heightened security – three days earlier, Marcus Sarjeant fired six blank shots at the Queen as she rode down the Mall to the Trooping the Colour ceremony.

"No Home Secretary's going to like you not recognising that he's the Home Secretary."

Daily Express, 16 June 1981

58 One of the bars in the House of Commons. It was reported that Margaret Thatcher was in a stubborn and defiant mood at the end of her Party's Conference in Blackpool the previous week. Michael Heseltine (walking with her) was Secretary of State for the Environment. After his defeat by Thatcher as Party Leader in February 1971, Edward (Ted) Heath returned to the backbenches and became openly critical of Thatcherism.

"I reckon she heard you say 'Hear hear' to Ted's speech at Blackpool."

Daily Express, 20 October 1981

Michael Foot, Leader of the Opposition, walking his dog, with Denis Healey, Deputy Leader of the Labour Party, swatting a wasp.
Foot need not have worried about being sued – Prime Minister Margaret Thatcher gained the biggest election victory since the Labour Party victory in 1945.

"It's from Maggie – she's going to sue if she doesn't get in."

Daily Express, 17 May 1983

60 Willie Whitelaw, in his hunting outfit, visits the Prime Minister at 10 Downing Street and is frisked. During an incident a few days earlier, while out shooting, he had accidentally stumbled and "peppered" two other sportsmen.

"Prime Minister's orders, m'lord – Frisk Willie."

Daily Express, 30 August 1984

The *General Belgrano*, an Argentinan Naval vessel, was sunk by the Royal Navy during the Falklands War, with the loss of 323 lives. During World War II, a German U-boat had torpedoed the British vessel *City of Cairo*, with the loss of 104 lives and 189 survivors, who escaped in a number of lifeboats. At a reunion of survivors at this time, it emerged that the U-boat Captain had directed them towards land with the words, "Goodnight, sorry for sinking you".

"No, Mr Heseltine, a U-boat captain apologising for sinking one of our ships is one thing.
Me going to say sorry for the Belgrano is another."

Sunday Express, 16 September 1984

Edwina Currie en route, under guard, to the Conservative Party Conference at Bournemouth, one month after she became Junior Health Minister in Margaret Thatcher's government. She already had a reputation for making outspoken comments and, here, the Prime Minister was taking no chances. Currie's damaging comments about eggs and salmonella, which finally brought about her resignation, did not occur until two years later.

"The PM says you can slip it off while she drinks her carrot juice, but back it goes before she puts a foot in the conference hall."

Daily Express, 7 October 1986

I feel that Grandma's advice on dealing with certain troublesome people at the time, with her experience of controlling the Giles family, might have been of some use to the Prime Minister.

"Thank you so much for calling and advising me on the changes I must make in 1987. Now hop it."

Daily Express, 30 December 1986

64 This time, the Prime minister is actually seeking Grandma's assistance (see previous cartoon). However, I am not sure that the future grandchild will be for ever grateful for the results of Grandma's appointment to the post – as illustrated by this cartoon.

"The lady says she's going to be a grandma and would you like a Downing Street job as an Advisory Executive?"

Sunday Express, 4 September 1988

Edwina Currie at this time was Parliamentary Under Secretary of State for Health and a natural enemy of Grandma, who would be greatly unimpressed by the advice about wearing a woolly hat, particularly as it would have meant removing the hat which appears to be a permanent fixture on her head.

"To avoid some grievous bodily harm get Grandma out by the back door before she sees who's just come in."

Sunday Express, 25 September 1988

Royalty

Viscount Linley, the son of Princess Margaret and Antony Armstrong-Jones, 1st Earl of Snowdon – a well-known photographer and film-maker – was born on 3 November 1961.

"As long as Madam appreciates that he's not a Viscount Linley and I'M not an Armstrong-Jones..."

Daily Express, 30 November 1961

The *Bloodhound*, a 19.2-metre ocean racing yacht built in 1936, was owned by the Royal Family from 1962 to 1969 to accompany their ship, the *Britannia*, in the Western Isles when they had their one true family holiday every year. Prince Philip needed it back to train for Cowes in August that year.

"The Duke says will it be all right if he borrows it next Thursday?"

Daily Express, 1 February 1962

Princess Margaret's husband, Lord Snowdon, was a motorcyclist.

"The Princess Margaret, Countess of Snowdon and the Rt. Hon. The Earl of Snowdon."

Daily Express, 8 July 1965

Admiral of the Fleet Louis Mountbatten was a British Royal Navy officer and statesman, an uncle of Prince Philip and second cousin once removed of Queen Elizabeth II. The Mountbatten Inquiry into Prison Security was established at the time of this cartoon.

"Earl Mountbatten is the most bemedalled leader of an inquiry into prison security – I mean he was the most bemedalled..."

Daily Express, 27 October 1966

The Queen and Prince Philip trying to melt into the crowd on the London Underground with, it would seem, one of them having offered help to someone.

"Of course, if you will go lending the coach to any Tom, Dick or Harry, dear..."

Daily Express, 7 November 1967

Is Giles suggesting that the Royal Family is falling upon hard times? No evidence of this can be found.

"Nothing gets on my nerves more than a bailiff whistling Elgar's 'Pomp and Circumstance'."

Daily Express, 11 November 1969

At this time, the government was discussing rent-rebate schemes and perhaps the royals were wondering if this could be used to their advantage.

"I hardly feel, dear, that because the sink at Balmoral hasn't been working properly since your great-great-grandmother's time, it justifies claiming a rent rebate."

Daily Express, 5 November 1970

According to Giles, the Queen, a great follower of the horses, supported the suggestion that the bookies should give more money to help the sport survive.

"The show must go on..."

Daily Express, 19 November 1970

74 According to this cartoon, which appeared on Prince Philip's 50th birthday, he was not keen on the event being widely advertised through the publication of books on the subject. It does seem unfair, however, to take it out on the Queen's corgi.

"Philip! It isn't Tiny's fault everybody is printing books about your first half hundred."

Daily Express, 10 June 1971

The Government was continuing its consideration of a national rebate scheme.

"Philip, did you telephone the council about this new rent assistance bill?"

Daily Express, 15 July 1971

It is well known that Princess Anne is strong minded.

“If HRH puts her horse down in that puddle once more HRH is going to lose quite a lot of my goodwill.”

Sunday Express, 29 October 1972

Queen Elizabeth, studying form, is oblivious to the ungainly removal of Giles's fellow journalist, Jean Rook, with whom the cartoonist had a running jokey "vendetta".

"I don't think we'll have much trouble from a certain lady journalist 'reporting the fashion scene'."

Daily Express, 19 June 1973

 Prince Philip's reputation relating to the press preceded him to Moscow, when he made a short visit, piloting his own plane.

"Only the Press, Comrade, they heard you have a reputation for being a bit of a boy when reporters are around."

Sunday Express, 2 September 1973

Obviously the Queen, as an ardent supporter of the Sport of Kings, was not happy to miss one of the most important events in the racing calendar.

"As a matter of fact I do not think this compensates for missing the opening of the Flat."

Daily Express, 21 March 1974

The Queen and Prince Philip are on a visit to Mexico. Prince Philip's sharp eyes have noticed the presence of an unwelcome intrusion – a hidden journalist with a flashgun.

"Careful what you spend, dear – third vase back row on your left."

Daily Express, 25 February 1975

Prince Edward was less than 12 years old at this point.

"Remind me to have a word with Edward about his girl friends phoning the Palace at two in the morning."

Daily Express, 13 January 1976

Princess Anne's first husband, Captain Mark Phillips, is referring to the straight talking for which both his father-in-law, Prince Philip, and his wife are well known.

"I see Daddy's set the fur flying again, Anne. Your turn next."

Daily Express, 20 January 1977

Prince Charles finds himself drawn into an industrial dispute relating to a staff canteen.

"You think he's lovely is no excuse to call Prince Charles to cool our canteen dispute."

Daily Express, 17 June 1977

Prince Charles on an official visit to Canada.

"I trust HRH Red Crow realises that last little ceremonial puff made my daughter the future Queen of England."

Sunday Express, 10 July 1977

The Queen wished to question the guest list which Prince Charles had drawn up for his 30th birthday party later that year.

"Fawcett-Majors Farrah – Trudeau Margaret – Hamilton Willie. Please come here a moment, Charles."

Sunday Express, 9 April 1978

Earlier that week, a painting entitled *Near Stoke-by-Nayland*, thought until then to be by the great Suffolk landscape artist, John Constable, was, instead, attributed by experts to his son Lionel. Prince Philip was keen to ensure that, in the future, the painting would not be attributed to him.

"Now you've taken up art, Charles, please pay special attention to the signature and avoid the same confusion as Constable and his son."

Sunday Express, 8 October 1978

The Queen and Prince Philip were on their first visit to the United Arab Emirates during their tour of the Gulf. Prince Philip was obviously respecting the message on the steps.

"Philip – please stop calling me Fred."

Daily Express, 13 February 1979

 Twelve days before this cartoon, Margaret Thatcher had become Prime Minister. It is reported that, shortly afterwards, she had tea with the Queen. Is it possible that the Prince's comments were inspired by the Prime Minister wearing a hat similar to that of the Queen on that occasion.

"At least there's no danger of the ladies wearing the same hats today."

Daily Express, 15 May 1979

In the autumn of 1979, during the "Winter of Discontent", the Birmingham car plant saw 523 walkouts in a 30-month period. Finally, Derek Robinson, who led the union at that time, was dismissed – some people in the country increasingly considered him to be a very divisive national figure. Although no record can be found, it is likely that Mark Phillips, husband of Princess Anne, had expressed an opinion on the subject.

"Mark – some gentlemen from Leyland to have a word with you about closed shop."

Daily Express, 16 October 1979

Is that Princess Anne hurling the abuse and could the unfortunate recipient be her husband, Captain Mark Phillips?

"Ello, ello, ello, – we can't have that sort of language 'ere, Ma'am!"

Daily Express, 16 September 1980

With parents Princess Anne and Captain Mark Phillips both being good horse people, it is not surprising that their daughter, Zara, should be introduced to the activity at an early stage here at Gatcombe Park House in Gloucestershire. However, she was only two days old when this cartoon appeared.

"One can't start too early."

Sunday Express, 17 May 1981

 Four days earlier, Michael Fagan had broken into Buckingham Palace and entered the Queen's bedroom. Giles is suggesting a possible extra element of security not necessarily welcomed by Palace staff and the beefeaters.

"Her Majesty appreciates your desire to ensure maximum security ... now hop off."

Daily Express, 13 July 1982

This cartoon shows Prince Charles and Princess Diana starting a six-week official visit to Australia and New Zealand. The Princess insisted on taking their nine-month old baby, Prince William. This cartoon allowed Giles to display his skill at accurately drawing military and ceremonial uniforms.

(Prince Charles, Princess Diana and Prince William arrived in Australia.)

Daily Express, 12 March 1983

In 1982, Michael Fagan made two attempts to break into Buckingham Palace. His mother suggested that he wanted to speak to the Queen about his problems. The following year, he produced a version of the Sex Pistols' song "God Save the Queen" and Giles is suggesting here that Fagan was trying to persuade Her Majesty to endorse the record to help with sales.

"Sorry to butt in again, M'am, but would you mind signing 'By Appointment' on my new punk disc?"

Daily Express, 28 April 1983

On his first birthday, Prince William was already displaying a strong sense of character.

"Permission to remove tomahawk from birthday present, Ma'am? HRH has already scalped the butler, the first footman, the second cook..."

Daily Express, 21 June 1983

Prince William, at 18 months, displays his early skill at hitting his target. As part of a craze at the time, Prince Charles had been "pied", while opening a community centre in Manchester, by 15-year-old schoolgirl Katie Slater – the Prince took it in good humour.

"But, Charles – you were laughing when that girl threw a custard pie at you!"

Daily Express, 22 December 1983

It had been announced that Prince Charles and Princess Diana were expecting their second child and Prince Harry was born on 15 September 1984.

"Diana – where did you put William's old pram?"

Daily Express, 14 February 1984

The Royal couple were on an official visit to Jordan amidst heavy security.

"Peace be with you, Ma'am, they're some of ours. Mixture of King Hussein's bodyguard and the S.A.S."

Daily Express, 27 March 1984

Did Prince William get that from Alf Garnett in *Till Death Us Do Part* or from his royal grandfather?

"That wasn't from *Bergerac* – I think Wills got that one from Alf Garnett."

Sunday Express, 13 October 1985

The Queen offers advice to Princess Anne on Prince Philip's 65th birthday.

"We suggest we avoid jokes about him qualifying for cheap bus fares and half price at the cinema now he's 65."

Daily Express, 10 June 1986

Prince Charles and Princess Diana on a visit to Saudi Arabia – Giles takes another opportunity to make a dig at his colleague, Jean Rook.

"One of them could be Jean Rook, which could be troublesome."

Daily Express, 18 November 1986

Earlier that month, Princess Diana described herself as being too thin and as "thick as a plank".

"Thin as a rake – thick as a plank – Prince Charles is lucky he saw her first!"

Daily Express, 22 January 1987

This was a charity event broadcast on BBC TV, in which several members of the royal family took part with Princess Diana as a spectator.

"They've come straight to Ascot from filming 'It's a Knockout'."

Daily Express, 16 June 1987

An unwise present, perhaps, for the two young Princes.

"You'll get YOUR ticket when your father learns what you've sprayed on my sergeant's back, Your Royal Highness."

Daily Express, 25 February 1988

The Duke and Duchess of York were on an official visit to Australia when she forgot the age of her first daughter, Beatrice, who was born two months earlier.

"Don't get caught on the baby's age again this time, dear – just say 'Under 21'."

Daily Express, 6 October 1988

Celebrities

Sabrina was an English glamour model in the 1950s who developed a career in a number of TV programmes and films. She was best known for her hourglass figure and beauty.

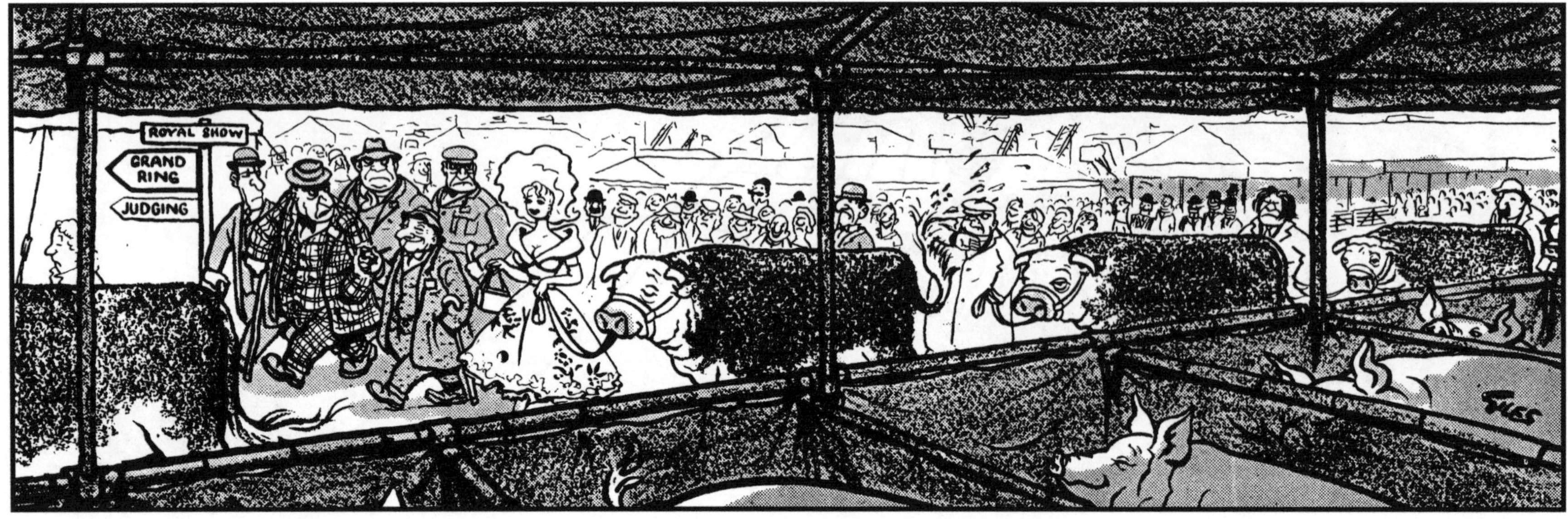

"You say hiring Sabrina to lead yourn in ain't creeping round the judges. WE say it is."

Daily Express, 3 July 1957

Alan Whicker (second from left) was a British television presenter whose career lasted almost 60 years. He presented the documentary television programme *Whicker's World* for over 30 years, covering both day-to-day and world events. Chancellor of the Exchequer Derick Heathcoat-Amory had presented the Budget two days earlier as "expansionist". I am not sure how the point made in the cartoon relates to this.

"I think it's a lovely Budget," said an average housewife. "Any Government that brings electric irons down from £5 to £4.17.1d certainly gets my vote."

Daily Express, 9 April 1959

Raymond Glendenning was a BBC radio sports commentator. He was noted for his handlebar moustache, horn-rimmed glasses and excitable broadcasting style.

"As they come into the straight, number one leads with a terrific right to the head – number two follows with a smart crack across the knuckles with his whip – another blow to the head – now it's number three who's in trouble! Number five's coming up with a beautiful right cross to the ear of number six – HE'S DOWN! and it's number two taking the lead – laying into everybody with his whip – ONE! TWO! ONE! TWO! – only one furlong to go before the bell..."

Daily Express, 11 June 1959

Giles is commenting upon a situation where the *Sunday Express*, owned by Lord Beaverbrook, had run a number of articles criticizing some members of the royal family, for "extravagant use of helicopters, yachts and planes". Prince Philip responded by saying "The *Daily Express* is a bloody awful newspaper…"

"The *Express* is a bloody awful newspaper," said the Duke. "Ah, well," said Lord B., as they trotted him off to the Tower, "at least he takes it or he wouldn't know it was a bloody awful newspaper."

Daily Express, 22 March 1962

Adam Faith (real name Terence Nelhams-Wright) was a teenage idol, singer and actor during this period and had many hit records. It is obvious that the British Medical Association felt he was a good source of information for their important investigations.

"Why bless my soul, Mr. Faith! Things don't seem to have altered one bit since I was a little lad."

Daily Express, 11 December 1962

Christine Keeler was an English model and showgirl who found herself at the centre of a national scandal. She had became sexually involved with a government minister, John Profumo, Secretary of State for War, as well as with a Soviet Naval Attaché in London – the situation was made worse by it being at the height of the Cold War. President Kennedy was visiting London and, obviously, both the UK and US security services were taking no chances.

"We won't detain you long, Miss Keeler. Just until all the American V.I.P.s are out of the country."

Sunday Express, 30 June 1963

Richard Dimbleby was a well-known BBC journalist and leading TV news commentator, normally with a very gentlemanly and mild manner. Just before this cartoon appeared, he was in Germany, commentating on the Queen's visit, when, not realising that the microphone was still on, he uttered "Jesus wept" after being told that the TV cameras had failed for all 30 minutes of the broadcast.

"Of course they're all on strike! Language like you bin using what else do you expect?"

Sunday Express, 30 May 1965

The 13th Duke of Bedford inherited Woburn Abbey and, in 1955, in order to cover heavy death duties, opened the Abbey to the public. This cartoon refers to unwelcome competition when the 6th Marquess of Bath opened Longleat House as a Safari Park, complete with lions, two days before this cartoon appeared. On Easter Sunday that year, 10 April, queues stretched back four miles with people waiting for six hours to see the lions.

"Anything Bath can do I can do better..."

Daily Express, 7 April 1966

The character Alf Garnett from the popular TV programme *Till Death Us Do Part*, played by Warren Mitchell, in a pub with Giles's most difficult character would be enough to give any publican nightmares.

"And bang goes the Lounge trade."

Sunday Express, 18 February 1968

Fred Astaire, in his top hat, outside Buckingham Palace, arriving for the final scene of *Midas Run* – a film in which his character is knighted. Elizabeth Taylor and Richard Burton were considered by some to be Hollywood "royalty"

"Of course, if Elizabeth Taylor and Richard Burton say it's all right to film Mr. Astaire on the throne at Buckingham Palace..."

Daily Express, 18 July 1968

Tommy Cooper was a British comedian and magician. He always wore a red fez, and was a large and heavy man, being 6 feet 5 inches tall. He was well known for his magician's tricks usually going slightly wrong. In fact, the fight that evening was between British boxer, Henry Cooper and the Italian boxer, Piero Tomasoni. Note the gladiator's outfit.

"Like it says, dear – the Cooper–Tomasoni fight will be broadcast live on TV tonight."

Daily Express, 13 March 1969

"Make love, not war" was an anti-war slogan during the 1960s. This cartoon appeared during the Vietnam War and shows a famous member of the Beatles, John Lennon, and his wife, Yoko Ono, on the poster. At this time they held two-week-long "Bed-Ins for Peace", as non-violent protests against wars – one in Amsterdam and the other in Montreal. Grandma obviously does not wholly agree with the concept.

"Vibrations from the 'Make War Not Love dept'. Grandma says if everybody isn't out of her bed in 3 minutes flat she'll be coming up to join you."

Daily Express, 27 March 1969

Bernadette Devlin was an Irish civil-rights leader and politician. Shown here in New York, she visited the United States in August 1969, creating a considerable amount of media attention.

"That's a bit thick even for you, Bernadette – telling them the jackbooted Callaghan has put Enoch Powell, Chief of the English SS, in charge of the Bogside concentration camps."

Daily Express, 29 August 1969

Lord Beaverbrook was a keen follower of horse racing.

"Women jockeys! Won't race in my colours unless I find her a matching lipstick."

Daily Express, 18 May 1971

Mick Jagger and his wife, Bianca Perez-Mora Macias. Presumably, the British businessman disliked Jagger's music more than the Pan Am stewardess did.

"Forget the stewardess who said she'd like to drop you off at 30,000 ft., Mick – Dad here says he'd like to make it 60,000."

Daily Express, 2 December 1971

Lord Longford was a British politician and social reformer. In 1972, he was appointed as head of a committee investigating the effects of pornography on society that published a controversial report on the subject. Giles is suggesting that the issues examined by the study went back a long way in human history.

"Psst! On with your fig leaves!"

Sunday Express, 24 September 1972

Alf Garnett was the name of a very popular character in the TV series *Till Death Us Do Part*, played by the actor, Warren Mitchell. Horse racing was one of his many passions, along with West Ham football team and the royal family.

"Anyone who has had as much to do with horses as yer actual Queen Mother will understand most of the words in your script, Mr. Garnett."

Daily Express, 5 October 1972

Three days earlier, a charity rugby match between England and France was held at Twickenham to raise money for an air disaster fund following an aeroplane crash. All on board the plane, including 18 players and supporters of the Bury St Edmunds Rugby Club, returning from an earlier match at Twickenham between England and France, were killed. Michael O'Brien, being interviewed in the background, was an Australian living in London, who had run naked across the rugby pitch during the game, to win a £10 bet. Police Constable Bruce Perry famously used his helmet to great effect in order to protect public sensitivities.

"For using your helmet at Twickenham for services beyond the call of duty, Her Royal Highness has commanded me to present you with a new hat."

Daily Express, 23 April 1974

On this day, veteran, comedian and film star Charlie Chaplin was knighted by the Queen. I am not sure if that is a guardsman imitating Sir Charles or Sir Charles imitating a guardsman.

"A very remarkable impersonation of Sir Charles Chaplin at the Palace, Guardman Davies. After his dubbing you will receive my standing ovation in the Guardhouse."

Daily Express, 4 March 1975

Kojak was a character in a very popular American TV programme about the New York City Police, played by actor Telly Savalas.
This cartoon includes one of his standard comments, but I am not sure saying it to the Queen warrants beheading.

"I think I can get you off the beheading rap, but I warned you Kojak, to lay off the 'I love ya, baby' when you were introduced to the Queen last night."

Daily Express,11 November 1975

 Pierre Trudeau was the 15th Prime Minister of Canada and father of current Canadian Prime Minister Justin Trudeau. Pierre's wife, Margaret, had many admirers. It is reported that once, in a restaurant, she sat at Mick Jagger's feet as he sang and stared at him worshipfully throughout the performance. A British newspaper later reported "Premier's wife in Stones Scandal". Jagger denied any links with her, but Giles is illustrating that Pierre had other views.

"I see Prime Minister Trudeau's got his man."

Daily Express, 11 March 1977

Derek Robinson was a shop steward at British Leyland for much of the 1970s and became convener of the Longbridge plant in Birmingham, having worked his way up from the shop floor. He led over 500 walkouts at Leyland's Birmingham plant during a 30-month period.

"Nice of you to come and explain to my missus why you're calling us all out just a few weeks before Christmas, Robbo."

Daily Express, 22 November 1979

The Bob Hope British Classic was the name of a golf tournament played in England every year from 1980 to 1991, except in 1984. Clint Eastwood is a well-known Hollywood film star renowned for his hard-shooting Wild West character.

"I didn't bring over 14 bodyguards for Clint Eastwood to use for target practice!"

Daily Express, 24 September 1981

John McEnroe was a well-known international tennis player, as much remembered for his confrontational behaviour on court as for his undoubted skill and artistry at the game.

"I am not prepared to sit all afternoon discussing the merits of bringing back hanging for umpires and linesmen, Mr. McEnroe."

Sunday Express, 26 June 1983

Giles obviously thought that John McEnroe's habit of complaining energetically against judges' decisions was not limited to tennis.

"Bloody McEnroe – he's not happy about the photo finish of the last race."

Daily Express, 21 June 1984

Selina Scott was a attractive British television presenter who, at the time, co-presented with Frank Bough the first breakfast television programme in the UK – *BBC Breakfast Time*. Both are shown in the cartoon.

"That wasn't funny, Selina – we allocate those sort of jokes to the other channel."

Daily Express, 7 November 1985

Robin Day, a television commentator chaired *Question Time* and also presented the BBC *Panorama* programme, which was the subject of a major libel case relating to one of its episodes and, at the end, the corporation capitulated and was forced to pay £20,000 to each of the two men involved and also made to pay their legal expenses.

"Gentleman at the back – with libel costs at £500,000 a go, please be careful!"

Daily Express, 23 October 1986

Mathias Rust was a German aviator who flew from Helsinki in Finland and illegally landed his light aircraft near Red Square in Moscow on 28 May of that year. Rust said he wanted to create an "imaginary bridge" to the East, to reduce tension between the two Cold War sides. Hess was a Nazi leader who flew solo to Scotland in an attempt to negotiate peace with the UK during World War II. He was taken prisoner and eventually convicted of crimes against the peace, serving a life sentence until his suicide in 1987.

"Only four years? You're a lucky boy – Hess flew a solo stunt out of Germany and got life."

Sunday Express, 6 September 1987

Grandma encourages the rebellious side of John McEnroe's playing style.

"Don't let 'em soften you up, Mac – get in there and give the umpires hell."

Daily Express, 21 June 1988

The TV weather forecaster Michael Fish, and his boss Bill Giles, came under considerable criticism when he failed to predict a very powerful storm, which caused a great deal of damage.

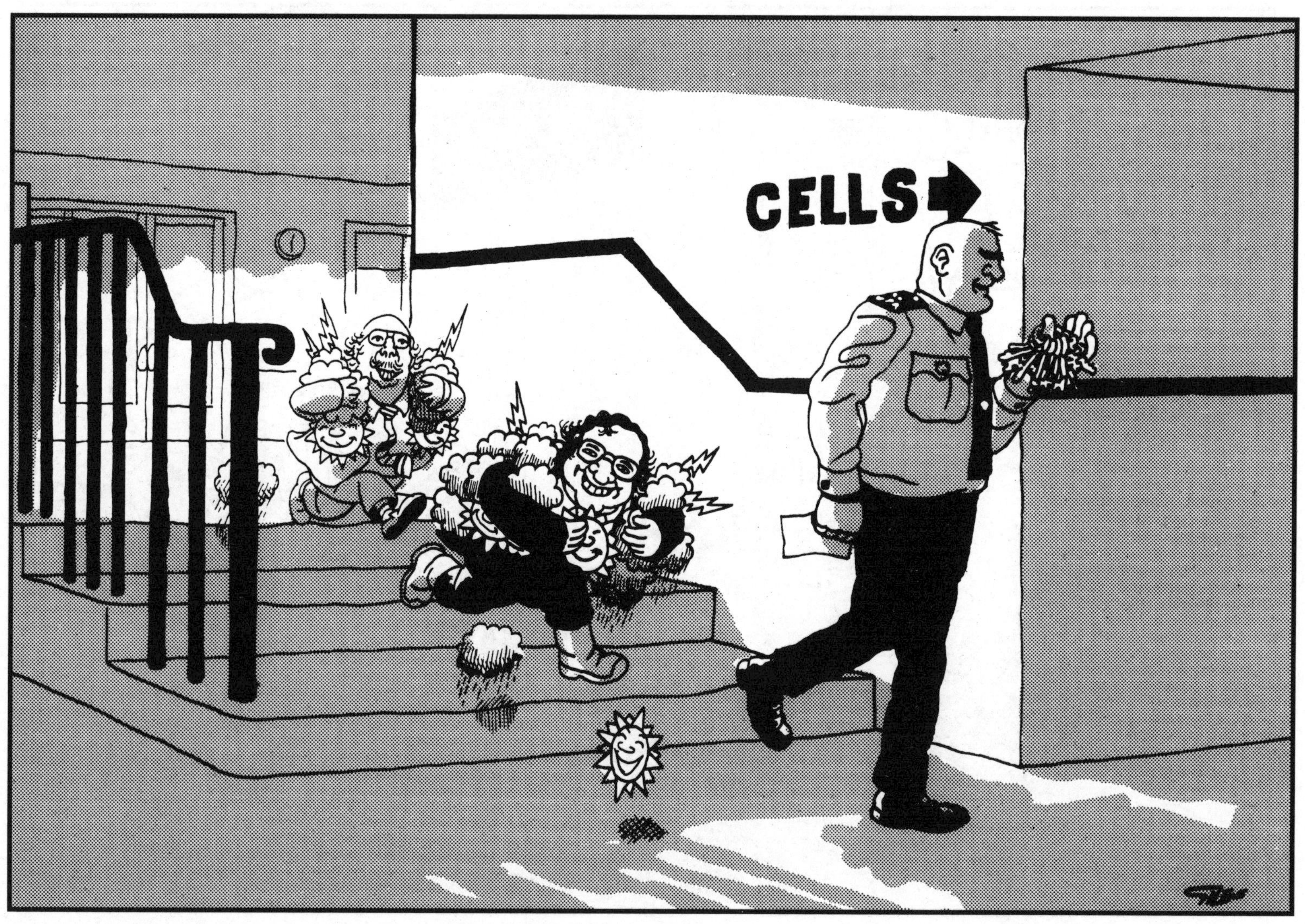

"If you're coming to us for protection every time you get your weather forecast wrong you might as well move in."

Daily Express, 28 March 1989

 British footballer Paul Gascoigne had just agreed to leave Tottenham Hotspur to join the Italian side Lazio for £5.5 million.

"Just because you alla come from Tottenham don't entitle you to da free tickets."

Sunday Express, 28 April 1991

Giles himself

Operation Market Garden – an airborne operation at Arnhem in the Netherlands during World War II – started on 17 September 1944 and two days later Giles was flown out to Belgium to continue his cartooning work from the Allied fighting front. Here, he is with his driver, Reg Bishop, just a few days after his arrival.

"Unsociable lot, these Germans, sir."

Daily Express, 5 October 1944

Giles at work under difficult conditions.

"Nearly had to do without a cartoon in tomorrow's paper that time, didn't they?"

Daily Express, 10 October 1944

"Night thoughts of a war correspondent sleeping in a Dutch hotel which was previously occupied by the Germans."

Daily Express, 29 October 1944

The winter was beginning to bite, adding to the difficulties facing the fighting forces on both sides.

"I'd sooner they sent us a few pullovers instead of cartoonists."

Sunday Express, 22 November 1944

The British Tommy was pointing out to Giles an increasing problem relating to the loss of the almost exclusive subject matter for his cartoons – of which, no doubt, the cartoonist himself was fully aware.

"Musso gorn, Goering gorn – you'll be in the cart when they've all gorn – won't 'ave nuffin to draw, will you?"

Unpublished, January 1945

Giles at work in his bedroom studio at home in Hillbrow Farm, outside Ipswich. Sir Stafford Cripps was Chancellor of the Exchequer at the time and responsible for tackling Britain's desperate post-war economic circumstances, which was a heavy responsibility. Giles is emphasizing the difficulty of capturing a smile, which, understandably, was rarely seen.

"Send up another lot of paper and rubbers – I'll get this smile somehow if I have to work all night."

Sunday Express, 19 September 1948

Another cartoon showing Giles at work in his home studio. His wife, Joan, is trying to tidy up while he battles with the decision about what subject he was going to comment on that day. Outside, the doctor and vet are shown arriving and leaving – so we can only guess that Giles is telling us that he is also beset with other problems – possibly expensive ones.

"What's it going to be for today – Hydro-Bs or pigeon food?"

Daily Express, 3 February 1950

Giles in trouble – simply seeking peace and quiet.

"Well, now, if it isn't Gipsy Giles, all nicely camped in a no-parking area." (Cheshire)

Daily Express, 16 May 1951

"I've chased you all over the Midlands with this, but I'm 'anged if I'm going to chase you all over the Lake District."

Daily Express, 17 May 1951

146 The miner may have been exaggerating a little – not long after this cartoon appeared, the industry began to decline dramatically.

"Miners get everything these days, pit-head baths, race horses for pit ponies, bulletins on Rita Hayworth down at coal-face..."
(Stoke on Trent)

Daily Express, 18 May 1951

It is said that beauty is in the eye of the beholder.

"Loovely scenery, ain't it, mister!" (Manchester)

Daily Express, 21 May 1951

The Dome of Discovery, which focused on scientific discovery, was part of the Festival of Britain, which opened at the beginning of May that year.

"Your Dome of Discovery's seen nothing 'til it's seen a coachload of us girls in London for the day." (Haworth Cotton Mill, Salford)

Daily Express, 29 May 1951

HOW GILES SPENT CHRISTMAS

GILES, recovering rapidly from pneumonia, thank you, thought you might like to see how his sickroom looked for Christmas

Here's a key to the carryings-on . . .

1 Healthy friends who heard I was a little better called in to drink my health with my Scotch.

2 Batch of Christmas aunts discussing ailments.

3 Grandma.

4 Another batch of Christmas aunts discussing ailments.

5 Healthy Cousin Andrew, who has a theory that the only cure for pneumonia is to get out in the fresh air and shoot something.

6 Anti-social Christmas aunt discussing ailments on her own.

7 Rush, who ought to have the same theory as Cousin Andrew, but hasn't.

8 Georgie, who has a theory that the more penicillin he pumps into the twins in advance the less chance they've got of catching pneumonia.

9 Me getting a little better.

A plague on your Merry Christmases.

"How Giles spent Christmas"

Daily Express, 27 December 1952

The Giles family's hopes of making a killing were dashed by his survival.

"Stop making holly wreaths, everybody – he's up."

Sunday Express, 28 December 1952

On the lane outside his farm near Ipswich. The big barn at the back has now been demolished.

"He said 'Happy New Year' to everyone we met and when they'd gone a little way past he said 'and I hope you fall down a hole'."

Daily Express, 1 January 1953

A past crime catching up with Giles.

"Thought you'd take the micky out of the Guards in last week's *Sunday Express* then hop off out of the country for a while, did you?"

Sunday Express, 24 May 1953

Giles was a keen motorist and here he is as the co-driver in his XK 120 Jaguar Roadster on a rally, with Norwich Cathedral in the background. This vehicle appears in a number of his cartoons.

"They're wearing smog masks so that their navigators can't hear what they're calling them."

Daily Express, 11 November 1953

The Government discusses seeking Giles's help with a national problem.

"Hold it, Mr Giles – that's not exactly what Mr. Williams meant."

Daily Express, 31 March 1964

Giles examines the route, with his characteristic drink and cigarette.

Programme cover for 1970 International *Daily Express* Powerboat Race.

Daily Express, 22 August 1970

Giles with his glasses in the middle of the crowd.

"We've got to do something to hold on to the customers in case ITV comes back next week."

Sunday Express, 14 October 1979

Obviously Dodger was well known as one of the local poachers. Again, I am convinced that that is Giles, with the woolly hat and glasses, sitting at the bar. This is a typical interior pub scene in villages around his farm.

"If Cruft's gave an award for the best retriever on my estate, we know who'd be supreme champion, eh, Dodger?"

Sunday Express, 15 February 1981

Giles, under the mistletoe, with the mother of his cartoon family.

"Come back the days when you could bundle them all down the pub out of the way."

Daily Express, 24 December 1987

"Won't make a lotter difference to Harry who owns the pubs – he ain't bought a drink since they disbanded the Home Guard."

Daily Express, 25 March 1989

All the cartoons in this book were copied from material in Carl Giles's own private archive, a huge collection of artwork, ephemera and correspondence, which is held by the British Cartoon Archive at the University of Kent. Carl Giles had been cartoonist for Lord Beaverbrook's *Daily* and *Sunday Express* for almost 20 years, when on 20 March 1962 the Conservative M.P. Sir Martin Lindsay tabled a motion deploring "the conduct of Lord Beaverbrook in authorizing over the last few years in the newspapers controlled by him more than 70 adverse comments on members of the royal family who have no means of replying".

Lindsay was wrong about the royal family having no means of reply. That day Prince Philip also vented his anger at Beaverbrook's campaign, during a press reception at the British Embassy in Rio de Janeiro. According to the paper's Brazil representative, the Prince declared that, "The *Daily Express* is a bloody awful newspaper. It is full of lies, scandal and imagination. It is a vicious paper."

When the *Daily Express* reported this the next day, Giles decided to treat it as a joke. He knew the royal family enjoyed his cartoons; they often asked for the artwork. This had begun in 1948, when Prince Philip was sent a cartoon on the State Opening of Parliament, and over the next few years Giles received a steady stream of requests from Buckingham Palace for original drawings.

Left: *Lord Beaverbrook is marched to the Tower, 22 March 1962 (see page 109).*

Giles drew the diminutive Lord Beaverbrook being escorted through the Traitor's Gate at the Tower of London, with a headsman's axe and block standing ready in the background. The caption repeated Prince Philip's condemnation of the *Daily Express*, but added laconically: "'Ah well,' said Lord B., as they trotted him off to the Tower, 'at least he takes it or he wouldn't know it was a bloody awful newspaper.'"

This was a brilliant response, which did much to defuse the situation. When Giles's cartoon was printed the next day, *Daily Express* staff were surprised to receive a phone call from the Queen's press secretary, with a message for Giles that "Her Majesty requests today's cartoon to commemorate one of her husband's most glorious indiscretions."

Giles sent off the artwork and in May 1962 found himself invited to "a small informal luncheon party" at Buckingham Palace with the Queen and Prince Philip. "I was filled with absolute dread," Giles recalled afterwards. "But as soon as she started to talk I was put at my ease...There were about half a dozen corgis running about in a completely uncontrolled state. Suddenly the Queen shouted, 'HEP'. It was like a bark from a sergeant major. The corgis immediately stood to attention. Then filed out of the room."

After the lunch Giles mischievously drew a cartoon of the guests leaving with corgi-savaged trousers. He sent it to the Queen, who returned her thanks through one of her private secretaries, noting that she was "glad that you got away without having lost, at least to the best of her knowledge, so much as a shred of your trousers".

After that Giles became what one *Daily Express* journalist called "a kind of cartooning jester to the royal family". By the time he retired in 1991 the royal family had more than 40 of his original drawings, the largest number being owned by Prince Philip, who shared Giles's anarchic view of the world.

The British Cartoon Archive, based at the University of Kent's Templeman Library in Canterbury, is dedicated to the history of British cartooning over the last two hundred years. It holds the artwork for more than 150,000 British political and social-comment cartoons, plus large collections of comic strips, newspaper cuttings, books and magazines. Its website at www.cartoons.ac.uk has over 200,000 cartoon images, including the majority of Carl Giles's published work.